SQUIRT
the otter

**the true story
of an orphaned otter**
*who finds
friendship & happiness*

Tracy L. Mikowski
illustrated by P. M. Richard

Talking Crow Publishing

Haines, AK

special thanks to Lisa Wamsley

Published by

Talking Crow Publishing
Haines, AK

Publisher's Cataloging-in-Publication Data
Mikowski, Tracy L.

Squirt the otter : the true story of an orphaned otter who finds friendship and happiness / Tracy L. Mikowski ; illustrated by P.M. Richard. – Haines, AK : Talking Crow Pub., 2013.

p. ; cm.

ISBN13: 978-0-9860287-0-0

1. Otters. I. Title. II. Richard, P. M.

PZ7.M55 2013
[E]—dc23   2012953543

Project coordination by Jenkins Group, Inc.
www.BookPublishing.com

design by Yvonne Fetig Roehler

Printed in Malaysia by TWP Sdn Bhd, First Printing, April 2013. Second printing, January 2014
17 16 15 14 13 • 5 4 3 2

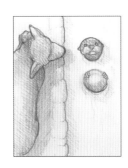

dedicated to Muffin
and all the amazing animals of Clinch Park Zoo

Squirt didn't know she was Squirt. No one had ever spoken to her before, much less said her name. All she knew for certain was that she was alone, her mother nowhere to be found.

Squirt called out, chirping as loudly as she could, until she was finally too cold and too tired to make another sound.

The tiny otter curled up in a ball and was nearly asleep when she felt a puff of warm air on her face.

Slowly, she opened one eye. A big black face with a long nose and whiskers was watching her, just inches away.

Squirt didn't move a muscle, and very slowly the face came nearer. A wet nose nudged her and Squirt cautiously looked up.

The farmer and his black Labrador, Toby, had been out doing chores when the dog had heard and smelled something unusual. Toby had followed his nose straight to Squirt, lying exhausted in the middle of the hayfield.

Toby gently scooped Squirt up in his jaws, holding the little body with the greatest of care, not letting his teeth harm her. The farmer had taught Toby how to be gentle with other animals, and Toby had safely retrieved lost kittens on more than one occasion.

Toby trotted back to the farmer and laid little Squirt down on the gravel.

The man gathered her up in his large hands and looked at her closely. "Toby, you've found a baby otter. She's going to need someone to take care of her. Let's go get you a treat, and then we'll call our friend Tracy, the zookeeper."

The farmer knew a lot about animals. He knew that taking animal babies from the wild is not usually the right thing to do, but he could tell this tiny otter had been away from its mother for a long time and needed help.

He put Squirt into a cardboard box lined with a warm plush blanket. Toby sniffed her one last time in goodbye as Squirt snuggled into the cozy fleece and fell fast asleep.

When Squirt woke up, she was at the Clinch Park Zoo in Traverse City, Michigan, and Tracy, the zoo-keeper, was just peeking into the box.

Tracy had doubted the small creature would actually be an otter, since it had been found in a hayfield so far from water, but when she reached in the box and brought Squirt out into the sunlight, Tracy realized she was mistaken! It really was a baby river otter!

"My goodness, you're just a little squirt," she said.

Tracy's constant companion, Muffin the Welsh Corgi, watched intently as Tracy gently examined the small brown fuzzy creature.

Then, cradled in the zookeeper's arms, Squirt looked up and chirped.

Tracy knew just what the little otter needed. She prepared a special formula, warmed it, and put it in a baby bottle.

Squirt drank and drank until her body was content and her eyes grew heavy.

Tracy put the sleepy little otter on a soft bed of blankets and Muffin promptly sniffed Squirt all over and then lay down next to her, protectively wrapping her strong, warm body around her.

Squirt instinctively snuggled up against Muffin and burrowed into the soft fur of her new friend.

Tracy and Muffin took good care of Squirt. As the days went by, they began teaching her things she would have learned in the wild from her mother. In particular, they taught her all about water. Water is very important to otters, but they're not like fish. They have to learn how to swim, how to dive, and how to hold their breath. Tracy began Squirt's swimming lessons in a small kiddie pool filled with warm water and Squirt's favorite toys .

Each day, Squirt splashed and slid among her playthings while Muffin ran around the outside of the pool, barking encouragement.

Soon, Squirt could hold her breath under water for longer and longer periods of time. Her swimming skills improved, and her coat grew thick and shiny.

Every morning and afternoon, Squirt napped in the zoo office and played outdoors in the fresh air and sunshine. Every evening, Tracy loaded Squirt into her crate and took her home. Squirt was learning how to be a river otter, but she was still too little to be left alone at night.

Squirt loved being with Muffin and Tracy, and she loved having the run of Tracy's house. The young, fun-loving otter stole the television remotes, the house and car keys, and various socks and stuffed animals. Then she tore holes and dug tunnels in the sofa to stash her new-found treasures.

Squirt also enjoyed digging in the houseplants, sending dirt flying in all directions. After uprooting the plants, Squirt would dive in and out of the bathtub, transforming it into a mud hole, and then slip between the sheets on Tracy's bed, where she would gleefully slide and roll until she was shiny, dry, and clean.

Tracy's house was a shambles, but the important thing was that Squirt was learning how to keep her fur healthy and waterproof.

Meanwhile, Squirt was growing rapidly and needed more room for playing and a larger pool for swimming. But even more than that, she needed another otter for companionship.

One other otter lived at the zoo. His name was Bumper, and when Tracy thought the time was right, she introduced him to Squirt.

Bumper was very good-natured, and Squirt instantly adored him. They swam together, played together, napped together, and groomed each other. From the moment they met, the two otters remained side by side.

One day, Bumper and Squirt were playing outdoors when Bumper decided to climb way up high on the rocks of their exhibit. Squirt watched as Bumper climbed higher and the zookeepers did their best to coax him down. When he slipped and fell, Squirt and Tracy rushed to his side.

They soon discovered that Bumper had hurt his back and needed to see a veterinarian. Bumper trusted Tracy, and in her arms he allowed the doctors to help him.

The veterinarians gave him medications and a chiropractor gave him treatments too, but in spite of the care he received, Bumper's injury did not heal. As time went by, it worsened.

Throughout this sad period, Squirt never left Bumper's side. She did her best to comfort and encourage her friend, but one morning when Tracy came to care for the otters, Bumper could no longer use his back legs. The weary look in his eyes confirmed what Tracy already knew.

Tracy gently picked Bumper up and wrapped him in a blanket. She took him to the veterinarian, who gave him an injection that helped him leave his body.

Her heart broken, Tracy stroked Bumper's soft fur and told him over and over what a good boy he was.

When she returned to the zoo and visited the otter enclosure, Tracy realized what a broken heart truly looked like: it looked like Squirt.

Lost and lonely without Bumper, Squirt wouldn't eat and seldom slept. Instead, she chewed on her fur and swam aimlessly in circles. The only time she was at peace was when Tracy sat in the enclosure with her and held the young otter in her lap.

Tracy tried to find another otter so Squirt would have a companion, but there were no other otters that could come live at the zoo.

Tracy hoped Muffin could help ease Squirt's loneliness. She let the two friends out together and they began playing just like they had when Squirt was small, Muffin racing around the pond, Squirt chasing and splashing from the water.

Muffin helped distract Squirt from her sadness during the daytime, but nights were another matter. Squirt was now too big and strong to run loose in Tracy's house, so she had to stay at the zoo while her friends went home.

To make the long, lonely nights pass more quickly for Squirt, the zoo staff spent hours each day preparing her sleeping area. They set up hammocks, crates, hollow logs, and sleeping bags. They filled big tubs with water, then added crayfish, minnows, and all sorts of fruits and vegetables. They stuffed cardboard boxes with newspaper, hay, and straw. Inside them, they hid things like frozen smelt, boiled eggs, and pieces of salmon. Tracy even put treats in the pockets of some of her old shirts and jackets and left them in Squirt's enclosure so that Squirt would have something that smelled like Tracy near her at all times.

Each morning, as Squirt watched, Tracy would clean up the monumental mess Squirt had made during the night. As soon as she was done, she would sit on the floor and Squirt would climb inside her coat to snuggle and rest.

One day, the headline of the local paper announced that the city could no longer afford to keep the zoo open. To her sorrow, Tracy was asked to find good homes for all the animals. She didn't want to say goodbye to her friends, but she was determined to find each and every one of them the best new home possible.

Tracy's friends around the country at other zoos and animal parks were quick to help, but she struggled to find the proper place for Squirt. If the little otter had to go somewhere new, without Tracy and without Muffin, it would have to be just right.

Then Tracy heard about a new facility in the Adirondack Mountains called the Natural History Museum of the Adirondacks. This was a beautiful modern facility, but Tracy still questioned whether this was the right fit for her little friend. Still, the main attraction at the museum was otters, and they had a wonderful place for them called The Wild Center that even offered a working trout stream!

After talking with Leah, who would be the young otter's new caretaker, Tracy realized she had found the perfect place for Squirt. Leah understood what the little otter had been through and was willing to work very hard to see that Squirt was happy.

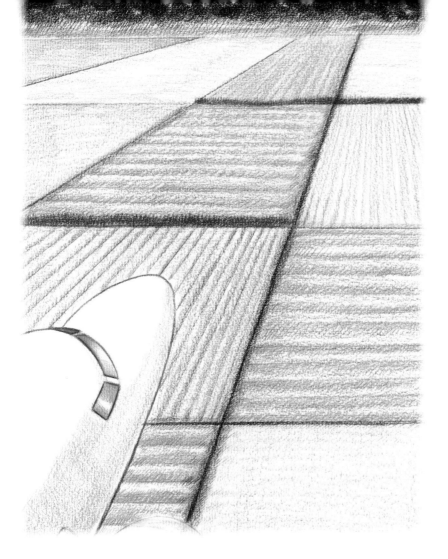

Now all Tracy had to do was figure out how to get Squirt safely to her new home. It's a long way from Clinch Park Zoo to The Wild Center, so she decided to charter a small plane. This was the quickest way to move Squirt, but Tracy knew the journey would still be hard on her friend. She was going to need some help.

After Tracy convinced Dr. Jerry, the zoo veterinarian, to accompany them on the trip, she made the arrangements. Then, very early one morning, Tracy packed Squirt into her travel crate.

Squirt was nervous, and everyone around her could tell. Otters have scent glands that, during times of stress, emit a strong skunk-like odor.

At the airport, they met Dr. Jerry and Jeremiah, the pilot. Tracy told Jeremiah how grateful she was that he was willing to share his very nice plane with a somewhat stinky otter and a cooler full of fishy snacks.

Severe storms over New York made the ride bumpy, but Jeremiah expertly flew the small plane around huge thunderheads, avoiding the bad weather as much as he could. Meanwhile, Tracy and Dr. Jerry tried to distract Squirt with treats and keep her calm.

In spite of their efforts, by the time they arrived in New York, Squirt's paws were raw from scratching at the door of her crate. She didn't want her ice cubes or her treats. She just wanted out!

The locals drinking coffee in the tiny airport were curious about the whiskered face peering out of the crate as the group exited the plane. Tracy wanted to tell them Squirt's story, but that would have to come later. They needed to get Squirt to The Wild Center as soon as possible.

When they finally arrived at Squirt's new home, Tracy let Squirt out of the crate, then sat on the floor. Squirt quickly climbed into the safety of Tracy's lap.

An otter named Squeaker watched intently from her cage while Leah, Squirt's new caretaker, asked Tracy last-minute questions.

When it was time for Tracy to go, she tried not to cry, but her tears fell anyway as she tried to explain to Squirt that she had to say goodbye. She didn't want to leave her friend behind, but her love for Squirt was so deep, it allowed her to do what was right for the little otter, no matter how much she would miss her.

As Tracy left, her heart breaking with sadness, Squirt pressed her face against the wire, her paws clinging to the fence.

It was a long, sad trip home for Tracy as she thought about Squirt and all the zoo animals she loved, but a short while later, she got a phone call from Leah that made her feel much better.

Leah told Tracy she had followed her heart and made an early decision about Squirt's care that was a bit unusual. Knowing that humans had raised both Squirt and Squeaker, Leah had introduced the two otters. She knew there was a chance the two females would not get along, but because they had both lost their people friends, she wanted to give it a try. Leah excitedly told Tracy that the two otters had become fast friends and had found instant comfort and companionship together.

Tracy was so happy that she cried again, this time tears of joy. Everything she had hoped for had come true for Squirt!

In the days that followed, Leah and Tracy spoke frequently about Squirt. Leah even sent videos of Squirt playing with her new friend.

As Tracy watched Squirt play a friendly game of tag with Squeaker, demolish a snowman the staff had built for them, and eagerly devour her fish and fruit snacks, her heart grew light. There was no question about it: Squirt was finally and forever a happy little river otter.

You can visit the otters at The Wild Center located in the Natural History Museum of the Adirondacks in New York State or online at www.wildcenter.org.

You can also visit their Facebook page at www.facebook.com/thewildcenter.

Tracy and Squirt

TRACY L. MIKOWSKI was born and raised in northern Michigan. She grew up with a family-owned animal park and delighted in a childhood filled with wild and domestic birds and animals. Her compassion for all living creatures became evident at a very young age. Tracy was a zookeeper for many years at Clinch Park Zoo in Traverse City, Michigan, where she lovingly cared for all the animal residents, including otters, wolves, mountain lions, bats, and porcupines. Tracy now lives in Alaska with her husband, Joe, and their five dogs.

P. M. RICHARD has had a lifelong love of art which was nurtured by his parents. As a child, he enjoyed drawing cartoon characters and superheroes. Crayons evolved to graphite pencils, next came pen/ink, followed by colored pencils and eventually oil paints. Pete currently resides in Algonac, Michigan. Family is his top priority. He is thankful for his wife, Tamie, and the opportunity to be a parent to both Kendra and Kyle. His most prized gifts are his two grandchildren, Jakson and Lydia.